RAMADAN AND E

EID KAREEM
Ameer Saab!

By
Fawzia Gilani-Williams

Goodwordkidz
Helping you build a family of faith

Once upon a time there lived a rich man named Ameer. He was called Ameer because he was so wealthy. Ameer Saab had the biggest house, the biggest car, and the biggest bank account. Almost everything he had was big. But Ameer Saab was a selfish man, he didn't like to part with any of his money! Because of this he only kept one servant, Raheem, and he would make him do all the cooking and all the cleaning. And he only paid him a very small wage.

Tomorrow was Eid but Ameer Saab didn't care. He didn't like *Eid* at all. "It's just a waste of money" he would mutter. Ameer Saab didn't even offer *Salah*, and he would never give *Zakah*. "This is all my money!" he would say, "And nobody's getting any of it!"

That afternoon after Raheem had served Ameer Saab his meal, he stood waiting to ask him a question. Ameer Saab looked at Raheem.

"I suppose you want the day off tomorrow!" he scowled.

"Inshallah, if you please Ameer Saab," said Raheem, "if it's no trouble."

"It is trouble!" shouted Ameer Saab, "You make sure you're here extra early the next day!"

"*Jazakallahu khairan* Ameer Saab," thanked Raheem, "and *Eid Mubarak* to you."

"*Eid*! Hah! A waste of time and money!" growled Ameer Saab. "Finish your work and be off with you!" Raheem quickly finished his chores and rushed off home to his family to prepare for *Eid*.

That evening Ameer Saab ate so much that his stomach began to hurt. Finally he called the doctor.

"It's nothing serious," said the doctor, "take a long walk and you will soon feel well," he advised. So Ameer Saab slipped on his walking shoes and began to walk.

Along the way he saw a woman holding a baby. The baby was crying and crying. "Please brother," began the poor mother, "I need to buy medicine for my baby. Please could you spare me some money?"

Ameer Saab just turned his nose in the air and walked away. "Pretending that her baby is sick just to steal my money," he muttered to himself.

A little while later, Ameer Saab passed a man in the street. "*Asalaamu Alaikum* brother Ameer," called the man trying to get Ameer Saab's attention. But Ameer Saab said nothing, he frowned and looked at the man, angry that his walk had been interrupted. "Brother Ameer we are collecting money for the poor, It is *Eid* tomorrow, would you like to make a donation?" "I have nothing to spare," replied Ameer Saab and quickly moved on.

Meanwhile Raheem was home with his family. His wife had washed clothes for their three children for *Eid* tomorrow and she had cooked some potato rolls. Raheem's family was poor.

Sometimes they didn't have enough to eat, but somehow they managed. Everyday they thanked Allah for everything they had. Raheem's wife emptied an old tin box onto the table. Out fell lots of small coins that she had collected all year. She picked up three coins and handed the rest to Raheem.

"Please go and take this money to the Widow Halima and to the orphan who lives at the end of the street," she instructed.

9

By now Ameer Saab happened to walk by a mosque. It was almost *Maghrib* time. But he did not go to the mosque and he did not offer *Salah*. Outside the mosque sat two young boys reading verses from the Qur'an. They read *Sura Ma'un*, then they read the translation. This is what they said:

> *"Do you see the one who denies the Judgement to come? Such is the man who pushes away the orphan and encourages not the feeding of the poor. So woe to the worshippers who are neglectful of their prayers, those who want to be seen of men but refuse to supply even neighborly needs."*

Ameer Saab heard every word they said, but pretended not to. He hurried down the road. Soon after he came to a thin boy dressed in rags.

"Please dear brother," said the boy, "please give me some money so I can buy some bread."

"I've got no money for you!" shouted Ameer Saab, "You lazy scoundrel! Get a job!"

The boy hung his head down and walked away with tears in his eyes.

As the sun went down, Ameer Saab got home, he felt much better, his stomach ache had gone. Soon after, he settled down to sleep on his big comfortable bed. But during the night he began to have nightmares.

First he saw his father crying and wailing, "Ameer! Ameer! Listen to me my son! Listen to my words!" Ameer Saab was terrified.

"My son all you care about is money! You never pray! You never give charity! You ignore the sick and the poor! O Ameer! If you don't change your ways, Allah will punish you!"

Ameer Saab let out a cry and suddenly woke up.
"O it was only a dream, just a dream!" he told
himself, "It wasn't real." Eventually he calmed
himself down then went back to sleep.

Not long after did he begin to have another nightmare. This time he saw a woman with a baby sobbing. "Help me! Help me! My baby is sick!" cried the woman. In the dream Ameer Saab looked at the woman, suddenly he saw the face of his mother. Ameer Saab let out a scream so loud that it woke him up. He was sweating. "It's just another bad dream," he told himself, It's just a dream."

After what seemed a long while Ameer Saab went back to sleep again. But soon he was having another nightmare.

This time in his dream his gold and silver were wrapped around his neck like a chain, he could hardly walk. Just then he saw the boy dressed in rags lying in a corner. He touched the boy's hand, it felt cold and lifeless.

Ameer Saab let out a thunderous cry, "Ahhhhhhhhhh!" and sat up on his bed with a jump. "O it was just another dream!" he sighed, he felt so relieved.

Ameer Saab climbed out of bed and washed himself and then for the first time in a long time, he made *wudu*. After praying and asking for forgiveness from Allah, he changed into a fresh suit of clothes and filled a bag full of money and a basket full of food. All night long he roamed through the streets until finally he found the boy dressed in rags.

The boy was sleeping huddled up against a brick wall.

Ameer Saab left the basket of food and a handful of gold coins next to the boy.

Next he began to search for the woman with a baby and not long after he found her sitting under a tree with her baby who was fast asleep.

"*Asalaamu Alaikum,*" said Ameer Saab.
"*Wa alaikum Assalaam* brother," returned the mother.
"Here, this is for medicine and for *Eid*," said Ameer Saab and he dropped two handfuls of gold coins near the baby.

"*SubhanAllah! SubhanAllah*! O Allah bless you!" cried the mother gathering the coins. She was so happy and so was Ameer Saab. It felt good to help someone in need of help.

Ameer Saab then spent the rest of the night slipping gold coins under the doors of poor people. Finally it was time for *Fajr*. He could hear the *adhan* and he walked in the direction of the mosque. When he got there he filled the charity box with money.

In the mosque he greeted everyone with *salaam*,
taking their hands and giving them all a warm shake.
Everyone was pleased to see him.

After *Salat-ul-Eid*, Ameer Saab gave money to the children around him and wished everyone *Eid Mubarak*. He saw Raheem and rushed up to him and embraced him. "*Eid Mubarak* Raheem!" cried the happy man.

Raheem looked at Ameer Saab in disbelief. He couldn't believe his eyes.

"*Eid Kareem* Ameer Saab!" exclaimed Raheem with his eyes and mouth wide open.

Ameer Saab gave Raheem a big hug and then placed something in his hand. Raheem watched Ameer Saab walking around and greeting everyone. He felt very happy. Then he looked at his hand and there lay five gold pieces. "SubhanAllah!" cried Raheem.

From that day on Ameer Saab was a changed man. He still had the biggest house and the biggest car and the biggest bank account, but he shared his wealth and never turned anyone away. He gave to the poor, the sick and the needy and he was always at the mosque to offer *Salah*.

Mash Allah!